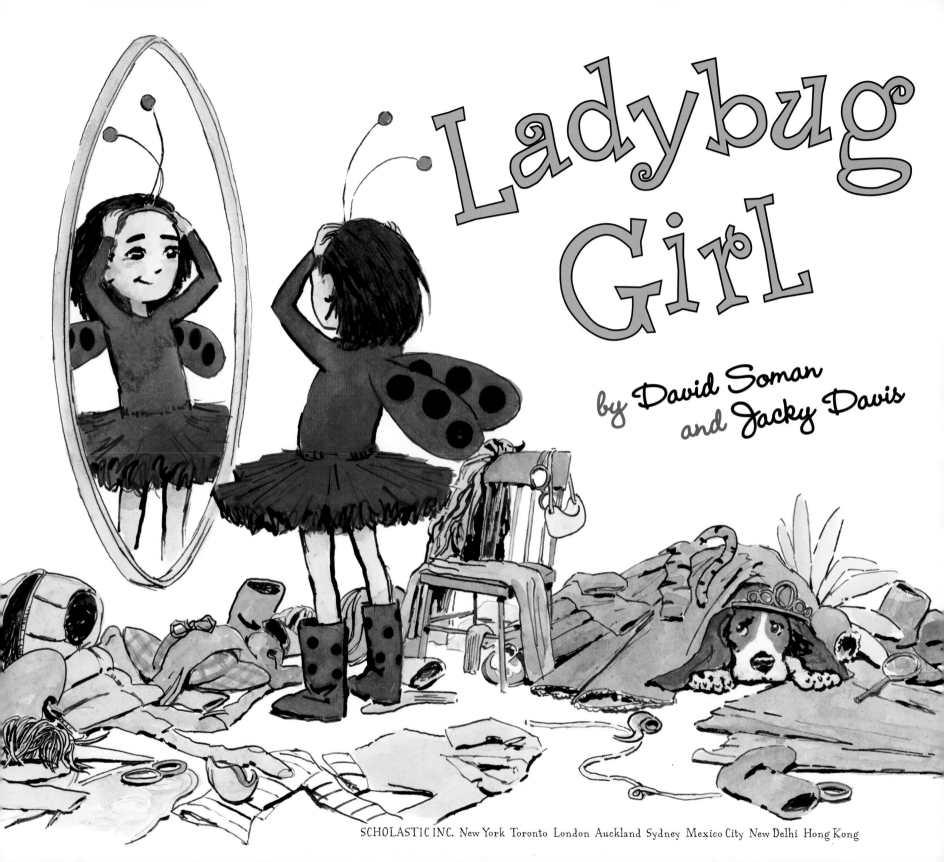

Ladybug Girl

by David Soman
and Jacky Davis

SCHOLASTIC INC. New York Toronto London Auckland Sydney Mexico City New Delhi Hong Kong

To our parents, for everything, and
to Lucy and Sam, for more

ISBN 978-0-545-22295-2

12 11 10 9 8 7 6 5 4 3 2 1   10 11 12 13 14 15/0

Printed in Mexico   49

This edition first printing, January 2010

Designed by Teresa Dikun
Text set in Aunt Mildred

"I'm Ladybug Girl!" says Lulu, zipping into the kitchen.

She slips into the chair next to her brother.
"Did you know that
ladybugs
eat
bugs?"
"Yes," he says.
"Everyone knows *that.*"

After breakfast Mama says,
"Papa and I have work to do around the house.
You'll have to figure out your own fun time, okay?"
"How am I **ever** going to do that?"
asks Lulu.
"You can do **anything**, Lulu.
You're Ladybug Girl!"

Lulu runs after her brother.
"Where are you going?"
"I'm playing baseball with Sam and Max."
"Can I play too?" she asks.
"No, you're too little," he snorts.
"And **bugs** don't play
baseball."

With a sigh, Lulu wanders through the house.
Bingo follows.

There's **nothing** to **do.**

In the living room there's a wall of books.
    Lulu can't read yet, but she knows her letters.
She finds a lot of *L*'s. More than 59, she thinks.

Then she waters her avocado plant.
    She takes out her ruler to measure if it's grown.
Some days it just doesn't seem to be getting any bigger.
    When Bingo gives Lulu *the look*, it's time to go outside.

In the backyard, the grass smells sweet
and is sparkly with dew.

While Bingo snuffles about,

Lulu discovers a line of ants
marching over a rock.

"Is that rock in your way, ants?
It's much too big for you to move,
isn't it?" she says.

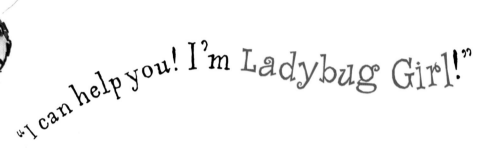

"I can help you! I'm Ladybug Girl!"

Ladybug Girl easily lifts the rock
over her head and tosses it aside.
Nothing can stop the ants now!

"Come on, Bingo!"
she says.
"Ladybug Girl
has things to
do!"

She runs across the yard to the pond.
Her brother calls it a puddle, but she knows it's big—
so big she can see trees and sky inside the water.
There might even be

a shark

in the deep part!

Ladybug Girl
jumps
in
anyway!

Her next stop is the old, crumbly stone wall.
It definitely needs her help.
She picks up the fallen rocks and
puts them back on top.
Now the wall is **bigger** and **better**
than before.

It's
the
perfect
fort.

Even the toppled-over tree at the back of the yard can't stop her!
Its roots look like angry snakes, but Ladybug Girl
skips all the way down its trunk, not falling even once.

She jumps down and lands with a bow.

"Ta-da!" she says.

Bingo wags his tail.

All of a sudden, Lulu hears the crack of a baseball bat.
She whirls around and sees a ball bouncing toward her.
"Hey!" her brother yells. "Throw it over here!"

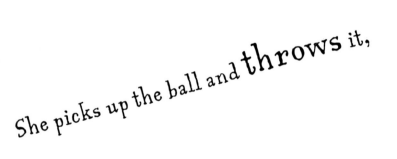

She picks up the ball and throws it,

but somehow it lands near her feet.

"Please can I play with you now?"
she asks when her brother runs over.
"No," he says, "I already told you, you're too little!"
He grabs the ball and runs back to his game.

Lulu
glares
after
him.

Lulu lies down, feeling the warm sun on her cheeks.

She knows she isn't too little.

She thinks of the 59 letter *L*'s she found, and how she saved the ants.

She wasn't afraid of the shark at all, she built the perfect fort,

and she balanced across the whole tree without falling—

all by herself!

From out of nowhere a gust of wind
swirls the air
with leaves.
She jumps up to chase them.
Ladybug Girl can catch leaves in mid-air!
"Ladybug Girl is definitely
not little!"
she yells into the wind.

Lulu runs up the hill to the apple tree and lifts herself onto a branch.
She can see her brother and his friends playing baseball,
and hears them arguing.
It doesn't really look like that much fun after all.
Not the kind of fun Ladybug Girl has.

She holds her thumb and index finger a bit apart
and squints through them.
She can fit her brother and all of his friends between those two fingers.
"I'm not little," she says.
"You're little."

Lulu sits for a moment
listening to the singing sparrows
and the squawky blue jays.

When she hears Mama calling,

    she swings down and says, "Come on, Bingo!

        Let's go inside and tell Mama and Papa about our morning!"

Feeling as **big** as the whole outdoors,
Lulu stretches out her arms

and flies down the hill with her wings bobbing behind her.